**INSTRUCTION TEXT** explains what your child will be learning on each spread and how to approach the activities

**DOTTED LINES** to trace throughout help to improve pen control

highlights that the It's good to trace the numerals,

NUMBER FACTS FOR 9
Help your child to write a correct number pair in the boxes on this page. Help them use this number pair to complete the addition and subtraction number facts on the opposite page. Then wipe all the boxes clean and do the same for another number pair.

Jack grabbed the harp and ran – but as soon as he touched it, the lovely music stopped.

1 2 3 4 5 6 7 8 9 10

The giant woke up at once and chased after Jack. Jack climbed down the beanstalk as fast he could, carrying the harp under his arm.

☐ + ☐ = 9

Draw around each group of items that shows a way to make nine.

How can we make nine?

9

## About the consultant

Experienced Key Stage 1 and Key Stage 2 teacher Caroline Clissold is passionate about raising standards in mathematics teaching in primary schools. She was a consultant and regional co-ordinator for the National Centre for Excellence in the Teaching of Mathematics, delivers in-service training for a specialist mathematics education publisher, supports teaching and learning in various schools, and has guest lectured at a number of London universities. Her aim is to increase children's enjoyment of mathematics, helping them to see purpose in their learning. She strongly believes in a creative approach to teaching so that children can use and apply maths skills in meaningful contexts.

6 7 8 9 10

d the
't there.

7

Draw around each group of items that shows a way to make seven.

**NUMBER ACTIVITIES** guide your child through the process of learning to add and subtract, step by step. It may be helpful to also let your child use practical objects as you work through the pages

**QUESTIONS FROM THE CHARACTERS** encourage your child to engage with the story and illustrations, and provide extra activities

**TICKS** for your child to trace when they complete each spread provide an extra sense of achievement

Well done!

17

Is your pen wipe-clean? Test it here:

1 2 3

Jack and his mum were so poor that they decided to sell their only cow. On the way to market Jack met a man who offered him two magic beans for his cow. Jack asked for one more bean – then he agreed.

How many beans are there **now?**

2 + 1 =

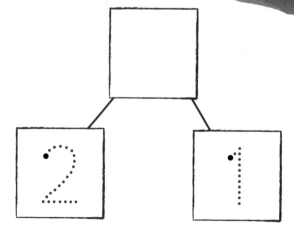

Jack ran home to tell his mum. On the way he saw some very strange things – magic was in the air.

To find out how many of us there are, add the number of chickens to the number of ducks.

How many birds are there **altogether?**

5 + 2 = ☐

5    2

Well done!

5

SUBTRACTING 1
AND SUBTRACTING 2
These activities explore the two models for subtraction. Help your child to write the correct numbers in the boxes.

When Jack got home his mum was so cross she threw one bean out of the window! She put the others on the table and sent Jack to bed.

To find out how many beans there are now, subtract the number of beans thrown out of the window from the number Jack had before.

How many beans are there **now**?

3 – 1 =

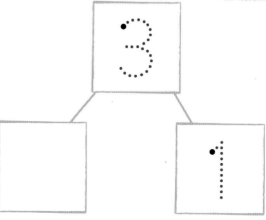

The next morning, a huge beanstalk was growing outside Jack's window. It reached up into the clouds. "I told you they were magic beans," Jack said to his mum. He began to climb.

How many **more** bees than ladybirds are there?

4 – 2 = 

4

2

Well done!

ADDING AND SUBTRACTING 3
These activities explore the two models for addition and the two models for subtraction. Help your child to write the correct numbers in the boxes.

At the top Jack reached a castle. He knocked once on the door. No one answered. He knocked three more times and a giant woman opened it. "My husband eats boys for breakfast," she said.

How many times has Jack knocked on the door **now?**

$1 + 3 =$

Three birds fly away. How many birds are there **now?**

6 − 3 = 

There are 7 flowers. 3 are yellow, the rest are red. How many red flowers are there?

7 − 3 = 

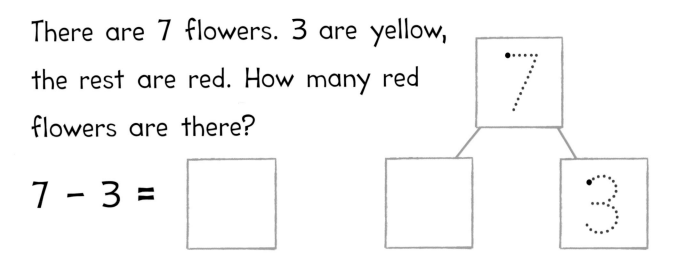

Jack and the woman both have patches on their clothes. How many are there **altogether?**

3 + 2 = 

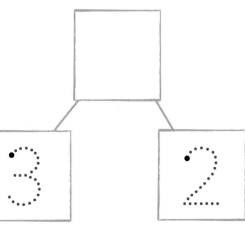

Well done!

9

Then the ground began to shake. Jack ran into the kitchen and hid in a cupboard. A giant man stamped into the room. "Fee fi fo fum! I smell the blood of an Englishman!" he growled to his wife.

Draw around each group of items that shows a way to make four.

4

How can we make four?

10

"Don't be silly, dear," said the giant's wife.

⬜ **+** ⬜ **= 4**

4 − ⬜ **=** ⬜

Well done!

11

The giant put a bag of gold coins on the table and then went to bed. Jack crept out of the cupboard and grabbed the bag.

Draw around each group of items that shows a way to make five.

5

How can we make **five?**

1 2 3 4 5 6 7 8 9 10

Jack rushed out of the castle and back down the beanstalk. His mum used some of the coins to buy five new cows.

⬜ + ⬜ = 5

5 - ⬜ = ⬜

Well done! ✓

13

A few weeks later, Jack decided to climb the beanstalk again. The giant's wife was not pleased to see him. "We lost a bag of gold the last time you were here," she growled. Then the ground began to shake.

Draw around each group of items that shows a way to make six.

6

How can we make six?

14

1 2 3 4 5 **6** 7 8 9 10

☐ + ☐ = 6

6 - ☐ = ☐

Well done!

Jack dashed into the kitchen and hid in a cooking pot, just as the giant man stamped into the kitchen. "Fee fi fo fum! I smell the blood of an Englishman!" he roared.

7

How can we make **seven**?

"Look in the cupboard," said the giant's wife, but Jack wasn't there.

[  ] + [  ] = 7

7 - [  ] = [  ]

Draw around each group of items that shows a way to make seven.

Well done!

17

Then the giant put a gold harp onto the table. "Play!" he growled. It played so sweetly that the giant was soon asleep. Jack crept out of the pot.

How can we make **eight**?

8

1 2 3 4 5 6 7 8 9 10

□ + □ = 8

Draw around each group of items that shows a way to make eight.

8 − □ = □

Well done!

Jack grabbed the harp and ran – but as soon as he touched it, the lovely music stopped.

How can we make nine?

1234567 8 9 10

The giant woke up at once and chased after Jack. Jack climbed down the beanstalk as fast he could, carrying the harp under his arm.

☐ **+** ☐ **= 9**

Draw around each group of items that shows a way to make nine.

9 − ☐ **=** ☐

Well done!

21

As soon as Jack reached the ground he called to his mother to bring the axe. As fast as he could, Jack chopped through the beanstalk. Down it tumbled, and that was the end of the giant!

How can we make **ten?**

10

22